THE WORLD OF KINDERGARTEN

THE WORLD OF KINDERGARTEN

CREATED BY CLANCY GOODE / PHOTOGRAPHS BY JAMES KILBERG

First Printing, August 1970
Second Printing, August 1971

Copyright © 1970 by Clancy Goode
Library of Congress Catalogue Card Number 76-118943
Lithographed by Anderson, Ritchie & Simon, Los Angeles, California
Designed by Joseph Simon

For my children: Kim, Eva and Pat

PREFACE

by LOUISE PIERCE

This delightful volume should really be entitled "Kindergarten Without Tears." When Mrs. Goode presented me with its tentative outline, I immediately assured her that she would have the complete cooperation of the Elementary Area West staff. My great enthusiasm for this book is based on the strong belief that a work dealing with kindergarten orientation will serve a great need for both parents and teachers. Too often we adults assume that going off to kindergarten is simply a "normal" step in the growing up process for all children, and we therefore fail to realise that it can be just as terrifying and overwhelming as it is exciting and new. To leave the comfortable confines of his home for the unknown world of the kindergarten can be a traumatic experience for a youngster unprepared for a classroom environment and its necessary routine. I sincerely recommend reading and re-reading this book to your child as well as allowing him to pursue it on his own in preparation for his venture into a happy kindergarten world which he can anticipate with pleasure and understanding. A joyous and worthwhile kindergarten experience is usually the basis for a successful educational future.

EDITOR'S NOTE: *Mrs. Louise Pierce is a product of the Los Angeles city schools. She has degrees from USC, UCLA, and Los Angeles State College; and has been a training teacher at 32nd Street and Brentwood schools, for Mount St. Mary's College, USC and UCLA. She was vice-principal of Brentwood Alan School, principal of Vanalden Elementary School, the original elementary area superintendent of the Elementary Area Valley-West for nine years; and has been area superintendent of the 56th Elementary School in Elementary Area West for the past four years.*

THE WORLD OF KINDERGARTEN

Here is a mother and her child going to school for the first time.
Let's follow them and see what it's really like in the world of
kindergarten.

The first day is Registration Day. Mother has many papers to fill out
with your name, address and phone number. Mrs. Van Duzer
is the principal of this school. Today Mrs. Van Duzer is here to help
the mothers and to tell all of the kindergarten children,
"Welcome to school!"

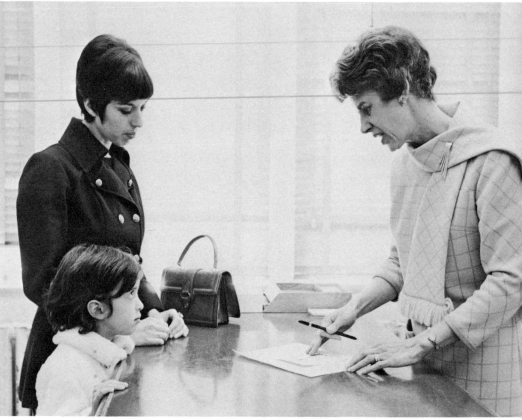

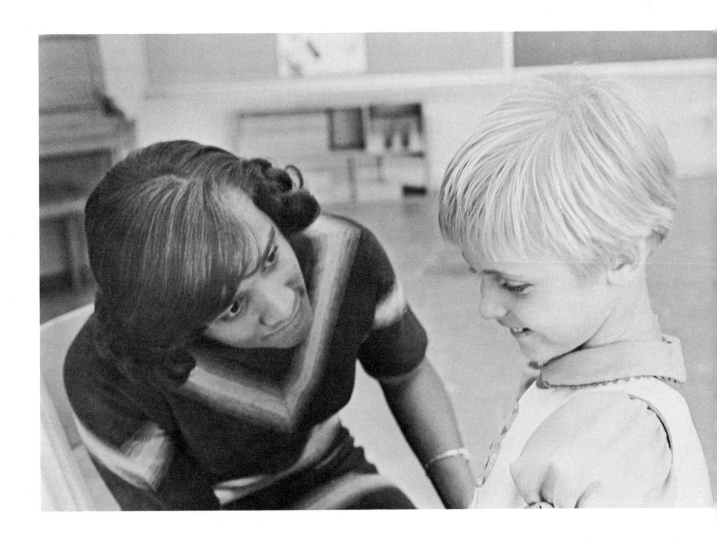

Since there are no classes on Registration Day, this is a good time
to find your classroom and meet the teacher. Then you will know
just where to go on your first day of school. Mrs. Corbin, the
kindergarten teacher, is saying "hello" and asking this girl her name.

At last! Today is the first day of school. Mrs. Corbin is explaining
to the children all the exciting things they will be doing in
kindergarten.

Saluting the flag is one of the first things you will learn how to do.

If you have something special you would like to bring to school,
you may. Pat has brought his plane and is showing it to John,
a new friend. Andrea has some orange beads and a pretty leaf from a tree.

This is sharing. All of the children are busy looking at Andrea's
leaf and beads and Pat's plane.

There are so many ways to make new friends: tying a shoe for someone who doesn't know how; or cuddling "Snowy," the kindergarten's pet guinea pig . . .

. . . or just sitting next to one another.

Learning to dance is another way to make friends . . .

. . . and it's fun, too!

Mrs. Corbin is telling the class that one day each week they will see films. Can you guess what the film is about today?

Everyone likes snack time!

If it is a nice day you can go outside to the listening center.
Today Pat has brought his favorite record, and he and John are
listening to it. Nathalie asks Pat, "May I listen, too?"

John tells Nathalie and Pat about the record he's going to bring to school tomorrow.

Of course, going outside also means playtime.
Wendy likes to play on the bars.

At playtime there are so many things to do! There is the sandbox . . .

. . . and jumping rope . . .

. . . and playing ball.

Every morning attendance is taken to see if any of the children are absent. Two children take turns carrying the attendance cards to the school office. Gina and Mark have their turn today.

It is exciting to do an errand
for your teacher!

When it is time to go home, Mrs. Corbin walks with the children to the gate. She stays with them until all the mothers pick up their children.

Some of the children go home by bus, some go in a car, and some walk. Henry is running to meet his father.

If mother should be late, Mrs. Corbin will take you to the office.
Mother will meet you there and take you home.

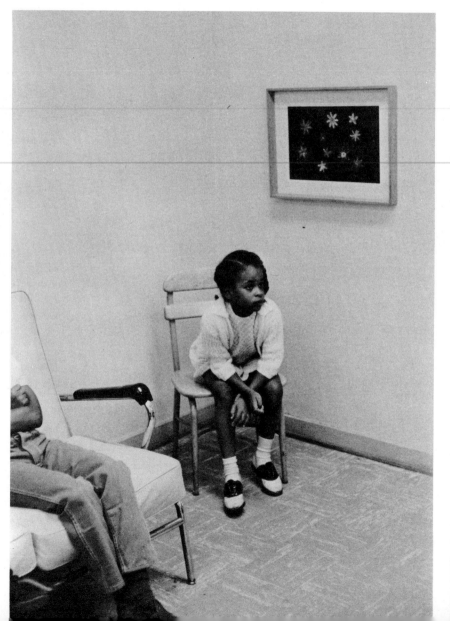

Today it is raining. Instead of playing outdoors the class gets
a chance to play with the building blocks.

What fun! The boys have built an airport.
Corey's plane is taking off!

Lisa and Tina are building a house. Tina is trying to decide if she wants to use the clock in her house.

When the children are through playing, it is time to put all the
blocks away.

Everyone helps. What a good job the boys and girls are doing!
Mrs. Corbin is so proud of them.

This is the beginning of a very busy week. It soon will be "Open
House." That's when the parents are invited to visit your room and
see all the work you have been doing. The children are outside
painting pictures, getting ready for the big night.

Andrea needs some advice. She is painting a fire truck and asks one of the boys if it really looks like one.

Lisa is making something from clay. John is doing a finger painting.

See how busy all the children are! They are working very hard, so that their classroom will look beautiful for their parents.

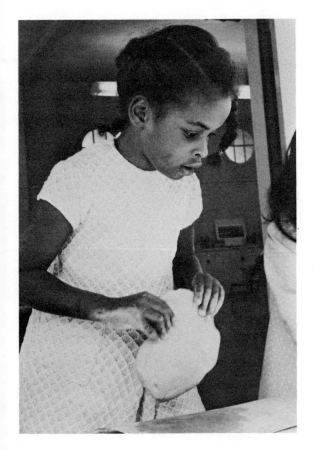

Washing up in the bathroom
is important when
you're through painting.

Now that all of their beautiful things are finished, Mrs. Corbin and
the children are deciding which ones to put up on the walls
for "Open House."

Everything is so good that it's hard to decide.

The big night is here! It's "Open House"! All the children are bringing their parents to school.

"Open House" is such fun!

This morning Mrs. Corbin is teaching
the children a new song.

Wendy is listening very carefully to the words. Now she can sing part of it . . . Hurray! She knows all of the song.

Mrs. Corbin is teaching the boys and girls how to use the library.

Kenny asks Mrs. Corbin how long he may keep this book before it's time to return it. Corey has found the book he wants.

Shh . . . they are all busy looking
at their library books.

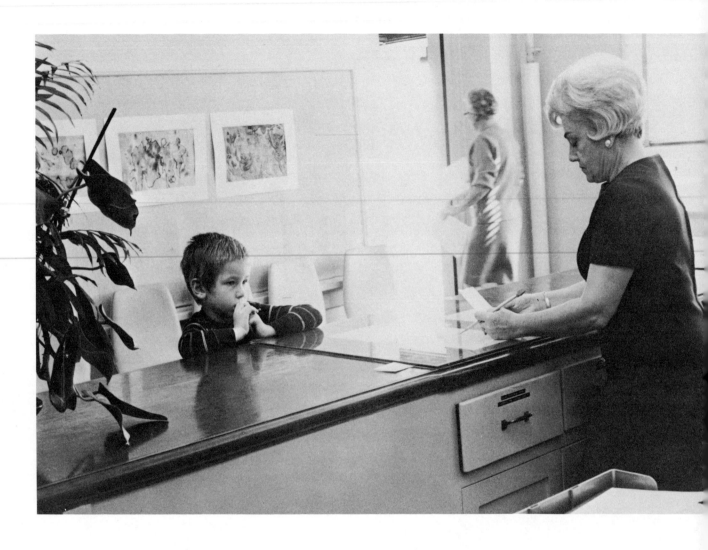

John has taken a note to the office from his mother. He was sick for
a few days and absent from school. Mrs. Berkov reads the note
and tells John to take the note to the nurse's office.

John is a little worried. This is his first visit
to the nurse's office. Mrs. Lansing is the
school nurse. She reads the note and gives
John permission to go to his class.

Story time is a favorite time for the children. One of the children
has brought a book and Mrs. Corbin is about to begin the story.

It's fun to watch, as well as to listen to Mrs. Corbin.

What a funny story!

When the story is over, Mrs. Corbin asks the children
some questions about the story. Some children are thinking,
and some are raising their hand to answer the question.

Today is the last day of school. Mrs. Corbin is giving the children
all of their paintings to take home.

It has been a busy, happy year.
We hope that you have
enjoyed your visit and that
you have seen what a
wonderful world kindergarten
really is!

We gratefully acknowledge the cooperation and assistance of: Louise Pierce, Area Superintendent, Elementary Area West; Mary Van Duzer, Principal of Brentwood Elementary School; Dan Reed, Principal of the Wilshire Crest Elementary School; Miss Johnson, kindergarten teacher at Wilshire Crest Elementary School; and a special bouquet to Barbara Corbin, kindergarten teacher at Brentwood Elementary School in Los Angeles, California.